A guide
for the
incurably
curious

text by **Marek Kohn**

wellcome collection

Inside cover: Figures from a 1734 edition of Giovanni Alfonso Borelli's *De motu animalium*, which used Galileo's mechanics to explain the action of muscles.

Title page: Caricature of Henry Wellcome as a mosquito. By Fred Reynolds, *c*.1900.

This page: Spears, shields and other weapons orginally belonging to the Wellcome Historical Medical Museum, laid out at the British Museum.

Opposite: Hall of Statuary, Wellcome Historical Medical Museum, Wigmore Street, 1926.

First published in 2012 by Wellcome Collection, part of the Wellcome Trust, 215 Euston Road, London NW1 2BE.

wellcome collection

www.wellcomecollection.org

Wellcome Collection is part of the Wellcome Trust, a global charitable foundation dedicated to achieving extraordinary improvements in human and animal health. The Wellcome Trust is a charity registered in England and Wales, no. 210183.

A CIP catalogue record for this book is available from the British Library.

ISBN 978-0-9570285-1-7

Commissioning Editor: Kirty Topiwala

Managing Designers: Anja Fouad and Marianne Dear

Graphic Design: Blok Graphic

Assistant Editor: Tom Freeman

Wellcome Collection and Wellcome Library photography: David Sayer and Ben Gilbert

Copyright and other information about illustrations appears on p. 112.

Printed and bound in Great Britain by Quadracolor, Surrey

Any omissions and errors of attribution are unintentional and will, if notified in writing to the editor, care of the Wellcome Trust, be corrected in future printings.

Clockwise from above: Henry Solomon Wellcome in 1906, painted by Hugh Goldwin Riviere; photograph in a head-dress, one of a series of portraits of Wellcome posing in fancy dress taken in 1885; Wellcome in 1887; Wellcome in yachting costume in 1886.

Contents

Foreword

Wellcome Collection is a place to explore the great themes and little details of life. Part of the Wellcome Trust – a global charitable foundation whose vision is to achieve extraordinary improvements in health – Wellcome Collection examines what it means to be human.

Like so much in the science we explore, opening Wellcome Collection has been a big experiment. Our challenge has been to reflect the ambitions of our founder, Sir Henry Wellcome – who amassed a vast collection of more than a million objects during his lifetime – while responding to 21st-century interests and medical developments. His collection could not easily be categorised: his central interest was the "condition of mankind" and he recognised that such a notion spans disciplines, eras and cultures.

Wellcome Collection responds to this refusal to be categorised: it is a historical treasure trove that reaches for the future; it is a showcase for curiosities and a venue for debate, drama and demonstration; it crosses boundaries and mixes together different perspectives, and it consciously embraces the rational and empirical nature of . medicine alongside the art and humanity of our responses to human health and wellbeing. We hope that Henry would approve.

We are a young venue compared with many of the great museums and galleries in London, yet we are delighted by the size and enthusiasm of the public response. We have welcomed more visitors than we ever dared anticipate. Many return repeatedly to our exhibitions and events, becoming our close friends and loyal supporters. We are excited that so many share our curiosity and passion for exploring the human condition through the lenses of science, culture, religion, history, anthropology, art and so many more.

So it seems the experiment has worked. Wellcome Collection is nothing if not irrefutable testimony to the fact that the human interest in medicine and health is as old and broad as humanity itself. Whether your interest lies in browsing our latest exhibitions and permanent galleries, attending our numerous and varied events, or consulting first-hand the material in the Wellcome Library, you are most welcome.

Thank you for visiting. We hope you enjoy what you find, and we'd love to know what you think.

Clare Matterson
Director of Medical Humanities and Engagement
The Wellcome Trust

Clare Matterson

▶
The Wellcome Building under construction on Euston Road in 1931.

Introduction

Henry Solomon Wellcome came to England from America in the 1880s and built an international pharmaceutical business based on tablet medicines, coining the word 'tabloid' to brand them. As he prospered, he devoted more and more of his energies to collecting objects, books and images, many of which are now part of Wellcome Collection. He died in 1936, leaving his company to trustees charged with using its profits to support medical and related historical research. The result was the Wellcome Trust, now a global charitable foundation dedicated to achieving extraordinary improvements in human and animal health. In 2007 the Trust opened Wellcome Collection, offering free exhibitions exploring health in all its aspects, and incorporating the Wellcome Library's archives and resources.

It's impossible to say where Henry Wellcome would have stopped if it had been up to him. He collected things that he could put in his museum of medical history; he collected things that represented different cultures; he collected weapons and furniture; he collected large numbers of things that were almost identical to each other. He collected anything that interested him, and his interests were boundless.

In consequence it has never really been clear where the limits of the collection should be. Today's Wellcome Collection has grasped this as an opportunity. Where the old Wellcome Institute for the History of Medicine once stood, Wellcome Collection now presents what it has called "the art and science of the human condition". The previous title echoes Wellcome's professed intentions; the newer

▶

Members of the Wellcome Historical Medical Museum's staff during World War I. In the first years after the Museum opened, admission was largely restricted to medical professionals, though male members of the public might be admitted if they had a letter of introduction from a doctor, and women if they were accompanied by a medical man. As the War went on, staff left for military service. On the far right, bracketed by skulls, is the Librarian, T W Huck; he was killed on the Western Front in 1918.

Burroughs Wellcome & Co. highlights its international reach on the cover of an 1895 price list. Silas Burroughs had begun to establish the London-based company's overseas networks soon after its foundation, on a world tour he undertook in the early 1880s.

phrase is perhaps closer in spirit to what he really wanted. Wellcome Collection commissions new artworks, digitises texts and images, and uses its imagination to make the most of the curiosities it has inherited.

Wellcome himself had been ambivalent about curiosities. He insisted that his original medical history museum, which opened in the West End of London in 1913, was to be for "intellectual and scientific study", not for people who wanted to see "'curios' for amusement". Nevertheless, visitors were treated to the spectacle of reconstructions featuring figures such as an alchemist and a barber-surgeon. Wellcome would not have got to where he did if he hadn't had a keen sense of how to capture people's imaginations. He was a showman drawn to science.

Wellcome was born in a log cabin in Wisconsin, then a frontier region of America, in 1853. He grew up in Minnesota, starting work at 13 in his uncle's drugstore, where he

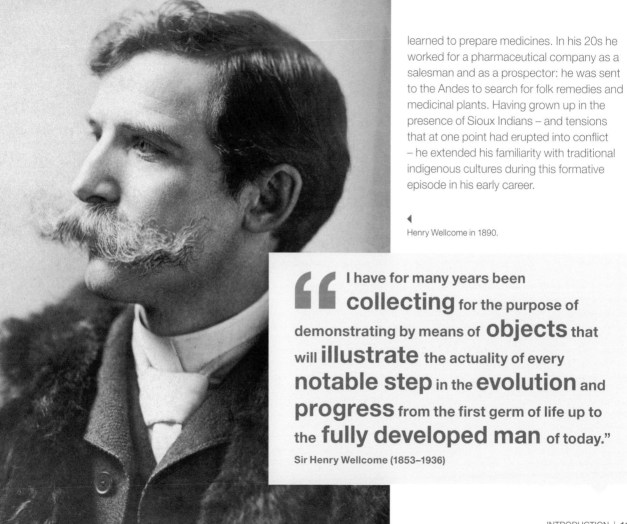

learned to prepare medicines. In his 20s he worked for a pharmaceutical company as a salesman and as a prospector: he was sent to the Andes to search for folk remedies and medicinal plants. Having grown up in the presence of Sioux Indians – and tensions that at one point had erupted into conflict – he extended his familiarity with traditional indigenous cultures during this formative episode in his early career.

◀

Henry Wellcome in 1890.

> " I have for many years been **collecting** for the purpose of demonstrating by means of **objects** that will **illustrate** the actuality of every **notable step** in the **evolution** and **progress** from the first germ of life up to the **fully developed man** of today."
>
> **Sir Henry Wellcome (1853–1936)**

'Tabloid' brand antimalarial quinine tablets.

◀

Burroughs Wellcome products on display at the International Medical and Sanitary Exhibition in London, 1881, the year after the company was founded.

In 1880 he came to London, at the invitation of Silas Burroughs, whom he had known when they were both pharmacy students in Philadelphia. They set up the company Burroughs Wellcome & Co., bringing a new kind of medical product, the compressed tablet, to European markets. The word 'tablet' was too commonplace to trademark, so in 1884 Wellcome concocted the word 'Tabloid'. By the 1900s this had itself become such an everyday word that a judge, while upholding it as a trademark, observed that it now referred to "a compressed form of anything from a literary education to household dwellings". The judge also remarked on how the company had sent Tabloid diaries to "every medical practitioner, to every chemist and to every known nurse in the Empire". Burroughs Wellcome prospered by pioneering modern techniques for marketing pharmaceutical products, trading on the Tabloid brand.

Wellcome became the sole head of the company when Burroughs died in 1895, and soon thereafter his collection began to grow.

▲

Henry Wellcome with workers at Jebel Moya in Sudan, where excavations took place from 1911 to 1914. As much a philanthropic project as an archaeological one, the venture employed about 4000 local men during the final digging season.

He and his agents stalked London's auction rooms and antiquarian bookshops like spies, hiding behind aliases – 'Hal Wilton' was his favourite – and even a bogus book-trading company.

In the 1900s he roamed across continents, touring Europe by car in search of material for his collection, setting up a tropical medicine research institute in Khartoum, and instigating archaeological digs at the site of Jebel Moya further south in Sudan. He and his future wife, Syrie Barnardo, the daughter of the children's philanthropist Thomas Barnardo, courted in Egypt in 1901; he renounced her in Ecuador in 1910, accusing her of infidelity. (After another ill-fated marriage, to the writer Somerset Maugham, Syrie achieved success as an interior designer.)

As he grew older he travelled less, directing his agents' activities in minute and rigid detail instead. Yet his larger vision remained

▶ The Hall of Statuary at the Wellcome Research Institution, 183 Euston Road, in the 1930s.

▼ The Hall of Primitive Medicine in the Wellcome Historical Medical Museum, 54a Wigmore Street, central London, 1913.

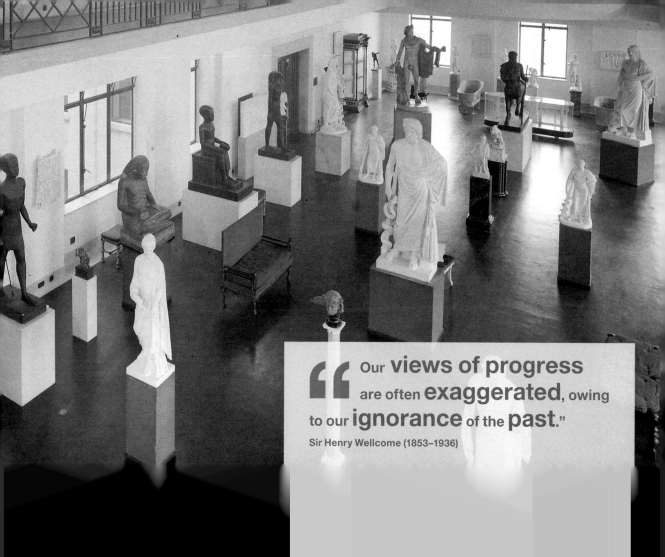

> **Our views of progress**
> are often **exaggerated**, owing
> to our **ignorance** of the **past**."
>
> Sir Henry Wellcome (1853–1936)

opaque, probably even to him. In the memorandum he left to his trustees about the future of his museum, he had more to say about preventing the furniture from damaging the floor than he did about the museum's actual purpose. His original museum had expressed his sense of progress, the Hall of Primitive Medicine leading on to the achievements of scientific medicine. But Wellcome did not dismiss the value of tradition: he recognised that many insights were embodied in non-scientific medical lore.

The Wellcome Trust came into existence upon his death in 1936. He had housed his research headquarters in the Euston Road building, completed in 1932, that has now been transformed with a sweeping architectural gesture into Wellcome Collection. Various museum exhibits appeared there over the years – what later became the Library's Reading Room was designed as the Museum's Hall of Statuary – but they were never more than piecemeal instalments of the larger project.

The underlying problem was that nobody even knew what was in the collection, or how big it was; people spoke of a million objects and half a million documents. Many items had been acquired without any supporting information about what they were, when they were made, or where they came from. "Curious object, use unknown" became a kind of catchphrase for the unfortunate curators posted to Wellcome's warehouse in one of north-west London's industrial suburbs.

Reducing the collection was the obvious way to reduce the problem. More than a hundred museums around the world became

▲

'Feel', by Antony Gormley, 2001. "Bodies may be temporary aggregates of cells but are also spaces which can be explored, dreamt and felt," Gormley observes. Like many of his sculptures, 'Feel' is cast from his own body.

◀

Flasks on the café ceiling suggest both modern biomedical science and the pharmacy tradition in which Wellcome Collection is rooted.

beneficiaries – as did several military home defence units, which received guns from Wellcome's arsenal during World War II. In the 1970s the remaining objects were transferred to the care of the Science Museum, where two medical history galleries opened in the early 1980s. The bulk of the collection, more than 100 000 objects, is kept in west London at the Blythe House museum store.

In the 1980s and 1990s the Trust increased the funds it channelled into grants by selling its shares in the Wellcome pharmaceutical company and diversifying its assets. As well as funding biomedical and medical history research, it supports a whole ecosystem of fields that contribute to the understanding and improvement of health, including art, medical ethics and projects that help the public to engage with science and medicine. Wellcome Collection, which opened in 2007, is the place where the incurably curious can explore all those fields at once. ⓦ

▼
'Silvia Petretti – Sustiva, Tenofivir, 3TC (HIV)' is part of Marc Quinn's 'Chemical Life Support' series, in which sculptures of people were cast from polymer wax mixed with the drugs they were taking to manage chronic medical conditions – HIV infection, in Petretti's case.

Temporary exhibitions and events

People often lend artworks and valuable objects to museums or galleries for special exhibitions. Jennifer Sutton, a 23-year-old woman from the New Forest in Hampshire, lent Wellcome Collection her own heart. And, three months to the day after receiving a new heart in a transplant operation at Papworth Hospital in Cambridge, she came along to see the one that the surgeons had removed.

▼
Jennifer Sutton looks at her heart.

The encounter took place at Wellcome Collection's first major temporary exhibition, *The Heart*, in 2007. Exploring both what the heart is and what it means, the exhibition combined science with symbolism, emotions and lived experience. Its successors have

◄
Troy Brown, British Body Building Champion 2007, flexes his muscles at 'Flesh', an event that also featured a plastic surgeon, a wax-effigy maker and a life-drawing tutor. It was presented by Materials Library, a trio comprising materials scientist Mark Miodownik, artist Zoe Laughlin and designer Martin Conreen.

►
'SleepDream', video by Johannes Grebert, 2007, part of the *Sleeping & Dreaming* exhibition, organised in collaboration with the Deutsches Hygiene Museum, Dresden.

Serena Korda's 'Laid to Rest' project collected dust from 500 homes, businesses and institutions. The samples were baked into bricks, exhibited in Wellcome Collection's 2011 *Dirt* exhibition, and then ritually buried.

continued in the same vein, using innovative contemporary art as well as Wellcome Collection's historical resources to provoke thought about the past, present and future of health.

Jennifer Sutton's reunion with her heart brought home how dramatically medicine can change the relationships people have with their own bodies. Five years later, the *Superhuman* exhibition, held to coincide with the London Olympics and Paralympics, suggested how people's relationships with their bodies could change in the future as advanced technology is used not just to repair the body's faults but to enhance its performance. Other temporary exhibitions, two or three of which have been held each year, have explored big, bold themes such as *Identity*, *Skin* and *Dirt*. *Brains* drew crowds of visitors to its powerful exposition of 'the mind as matter'. *High Society* considered the allure of psychoactive drugs rather than their consequences for health. *Ars Moriendi* and *Life Before Death* reflected upon how people live the last stages of their lives. Performance artist Bobby Baker exhibited the 'diary drawings' she made while undergoing psychiatric treatment.

In 2008, *Skeletons: London's buried bones* presented a group of skeletons chosen from among the 17 000 in the care of the Museum of London, using modern forensic techniques to reveal glimpses of people's lives and deaths over 1600 years of London's history. As Ken Arnold, the Wellcome Trust's Head of Public Programmes, observed, *Skeletons* was "about how the scientific study of bones can add to rather than detract from our emotional encounters with this material".

While *Skeletons* looked at the marks life had left on people's remains, *Miracles and Charms* looked at how people's beliefs have sustained them through life. This double show combined *Charmed Life*, whose centrepiece was a sinuous river of amulets arranged by the artist Felicity Powell, with *Infinitas Gracias*, a display of Mexican votive paintings depicting the 'miraculous' survivors of a great range of misfortunes.

▶

The portraits in *Life Before Death* (2008) were taken in pairs: one near the end of life and one after death. They record the time photographer Walter Schels and journalist Beate Lakotta spent with 24 people in the last weeks of terminal illness.

Infinitas Gracias: Mexican miracle paintings (2011–12) displayed more than 100 small paintings depicting accidents, assaults, injuries and illnesses in dramatic detail. People offered these images in pious gratitude to the saints whom they thanked for saving them from the misfortunes illustrated.

Brains: The mind as matter (2012) treated brains not as vessels for the self or interfaces with the soul, but as objects that can be measured, collected, probed and sliced.

Besides its exhibitions, Wellcome Collection hosts a continual succession of events ranging from symposia to supper salons, 'packed lunch' talks and Friday-evening festivals that enjoy the run of the building's public areas. At one time or another, visitors have been able to make offerings for the Mexican Day of the Dead and to question Papworth surgeons via a video link during an open-heart operation. Discussion events include 'Exchanges at the Frontier', a series of conversations between the philosopher A C Grayling and leading scientists such

as the biologist Sir Paul Nurse and the neuroscientist V S Ramachandran, presented in partnership with the BBC World Service.

Locally, Wellcome Collection has become part of the community. It holds midsummer picnics for Camden residents, and is a popular venue for students in Bloomsbury's university quarter. In the summer of 2010 a group of young people from Camden Summer University spent a week at Wellcome Collection working with an artist to produce graphic novels inspired by the

Medicine Man gallery; these later became the *Graphic Tales* exhibition. Another group of local young people used the *Miracles and Charms* exhibitions as inspiration for creating their own charms, which were hung on a tree in Russell Square as part of the Bloomsbury Festival, and later in Wellcome Collection itself.

Activities like these reflect Wellcome Collection's keenness to inspire young minds. Its Youth Programme offers school

visitors gallery tours and study days: one of these draws on the Library's extensive HIV/AIDS poster collection to look at public health campaigns and sexual health, while another uses exhibits in the permanent galleries to explore attitudes to body image, past and present. ⓦ

▼

The Lightswitch Project, exploring what happens when a light is switched on; conducted at 'Shifts in Perception', an event associated with the exhibition *From Atoms to Patterns*.

Medicine
Man

Henry Wellcome liked to recall how, as a very young child, he had found what his father explained was an ancient stone arrowhead, an example of a technology more important to its makers than the telegraphs and steam engines of his day. That inspired his imagination – and it also taught him how to use an object to tell a story.

In later life he aspired to tell an epic story of medicine's progress, featuring massed ranks of objects such as the 24 000 surgical instruments he accumulated. Many of his objects are arrestingly singular, though. They hint at tales of mystery and imagination – not least because of their unknown provenance. In spirit they are close to the 'cabinets of curiosities' from which modern museums evolved, and by which the *Medicine Man* gallery is inspired.

◀

Masks have many uses: those collected by Henry Wellcome include ones made for ritual dancers, healers, shamans, exorcists, executioners and victims of torture.

As displays are changed periodically, the objects featured in these pages may not all correspond exactly to what is on show in the galleries at any one time.

Some of the objects in *Medicine Man*, such as Darwin's walking-stick and Florence Nightingale's moccasins, betray an attraction to celebrity. The lock said to be of King George III's hair provided an opportunity to elaborate the story of his madness, when chemical analysis revealed high levels of arsenic that may have aggravated his condition.

Wellcome was also fascinated by images, both historical and contemporary. His collection is rich in photographs of peoples whose ways of life were being transformed by the activities of settlers, explorers and entrepreneurs such as him.

When he died, he turned out to have been carrying a miniature collection about his person. Several dozen photographs were found in his pockets: they included pictures of his deputy, George Pearson, and his secretary, Ada Misner, who was perhaps the most important figure in his later years. Wellcome's own story was in the end a lonely one. But his collection tells of countless lives and what they have in common, in sickness and health. Ⓦ

Beginning of life

Sex, fertility, conception and birth

The beginning of life involves fertility, sexuality, birth and the care of infants. It is attended by extremes of pleasure and pain, of power and vulnerability. In some cultures sexuality and the parts of the body associated with it are steeped in shame; in others they are put on public display.

These contrasts are richly represented in Henry Wellcome's extensive collection of material related to the beginning of life and all that surrounds it. Some of the objects and images seem to celebrate sexuality while others are designed to suppress it; some of them were concealed inside cases while others were hung outside buildings. Although many of the sexual images are explicit, their purposes remain elusive. Who were they intended for, and what did they mean to them? What kinds of relationships between the sexes did they represent? Here they are curiosities; were they also curiosities to the people who saw them first?

A clearer picture emerges from the images and figures that revealed the interior of women's bodies to show the anatomy of childbirth. These devices were used by medical men as they took over the

Phallic amulets symbolised fertility and strength in the Graeco-Roman world. As well as being worn, they were hung up in courtyards to chime in the wind.

In the 19th century, masturbation was believed to cause insanity as well as moral and physical degeneration. Devices such as the jugum penis were used to discourage it in mental institutions.

Porcelain fruit and vegetables, from China, conceal miniature couples engaged in sexual activity.

Chastity belts were said to have been a medieval technology, like knights' armour, designed to enforce men's sexual monopolies over their wives. Researchers now think this may be a myth: this example probably dates from the 19th century.

management of pregnancy from midwives and the mothers themselves. These objects were part of medicine's expansion, making increasing use of scientific techniques, into areas of life and health that had hitherto been governed by folk wisdom. Like the rest of the material concerned with birth and infants, they affirm that the beginning is in many ways the hardest part of life, and the most demanding. ⬡

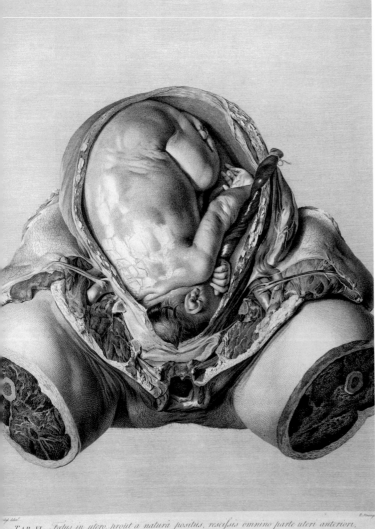

TAB. VI. *Fœtus in utero, prout a naturâ positus, rescissis omnino parte uteri anteriori, ac Placentâ, ei adhærente.*

◀ "The child in the womb, in its natural situation" – Jan van Rymsdyk, from an atlas of pregnancy by the anatomist William Hunter, 1774.

▲ Sex-aid kit from Japan, 1930s.

▲ Nipple shields to ease breastfeeding, made of ivory, glass and silver; the latter is hallmarked with an image of King George III's head.

▲
Still life and secret sex from
19th-century Italy: slid out of
its frame, a painting of flowers
reveals erotic miniatures.

▶
Childbirth in Europe, c.1800.
A midwife delivers the baby
while a second woman,
possibly representing
hygiene, prepares to
wash it.

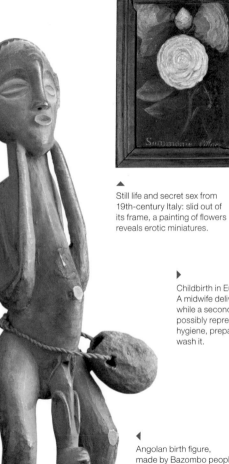

◀
Angolan birth figure,
made by Bazombo people.

End of life

Keeping death in mind

Death demands markers: memorials, relics and reminders of mortality. Medieval Londoners who died of plague were buried hastily in mass graves, but even then a token lead cross was placed on each body. Over the centuries the living were enjoined to be mindful of death by memento mori images, warning them to prepare for the eternity after it. Those tempted to take pride in their vigour or beauty were confronted with images of bodies at once dead and alive, one half glowing with health and the other ravaged by decomposition.

The living also had mementos of the dead, such as death masks and the brooches made from the hair of the

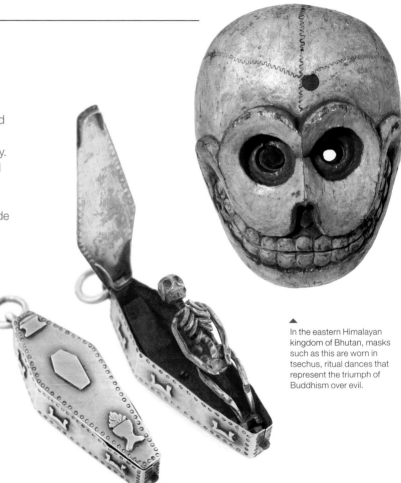

▶ Memento mori: a silver skeleton inside a gold coffin, worn as a pendant in the 18th century to remind the wearer of the transience of wealth and the shortness of life.

▲ In the eastern Himalayan kingdom of Bhutan, masks such as this are worn in tsechus, ritual dances that represent the triumph of Buddhism over evil.

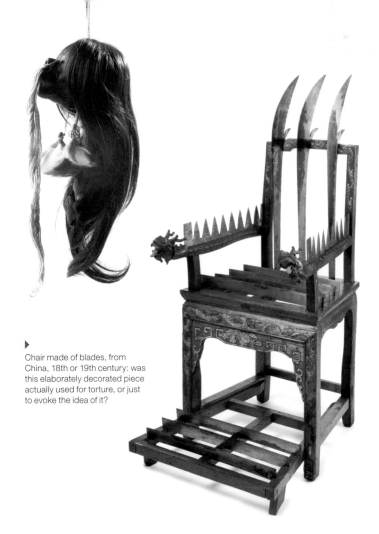

▶

Shrunken head, or tsantsa, made by Shuar people of the Ecuador–Peru border region. The Shuar made tsantsas to trap their enemies' spirits, whose power they conducted rituals to extract.

deceased that were worn by Victorian women. University College London has the body of the philosopher Jeremy Bentham, seated, dressed and on display. Bentham wanted to show that the dissected human body was "more beautiful than any other piece of mechanism". Wellcome Collection has a piece of his skin.

It shares a showcase in *Medicine Man* with a guillotine blade and an apparatus for reviving the drowned, objects that share a concern about precisely when death occurs. The resuscitator was based on the recognition that apparently dead people may still be alive; the guillotine was devised as a humane means of execution, but gave rise to stories that life persisted for a while in severed heads. Medical scientists tested guillotined heads extensively but found no signs of consciousness. The question remains open. ⓦ

▶

Chair made of blades, from China, 18th or 19th century: was this elaborately decorated piece actually used for torture, or just to evoke the idea of it?

Silver skeletons with a reaper's scythe and a gravedigger's spade affirm that valuables cannot be enjoyed for very long.

A lock of hair said to have come from the head of King George III.

Jewellery made from hair, popular in the 18th and 19th centuries, lent itself to mourning, allowing the bereaved to wear mementos crafted from the hair of the deceased. Victorian convention permitted women to wear hairwork jewellery after a year and a day had elapsed since the death.

Canopic jars were used in ancient Egypt to preserve lungs, stomachs, livers and intestines taken from bodies during mummification.

Memento mori figures from Regency England.

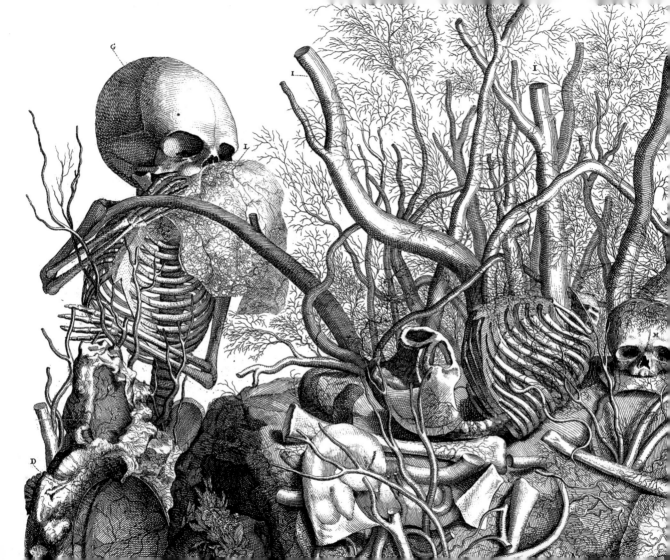

> **My body** I give to my dear friend Doctor Southwood Smith ... The **skeleton** he will cause to be put together in such manner as that the whole figure may be seated in a **chair** usually occupied by me when **living** in the attitude in which I am sitting when **engaged** in **thought** ..."
>
> **Jeremy Bentham (1748–1832)**

◄

Frederik Ruysch set fetal specimens in a macabre tableau for his *Thesaurus anatomicus octavus,* published in 1709. The skeletons themselves are preserved at the Academy of Sciences in St Petersburg.

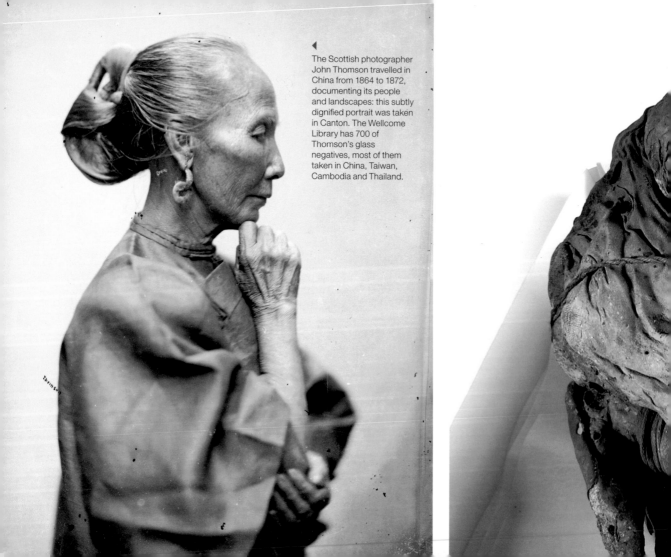

The Scottish photographer John Thomson travelled in China from 1864 to 1872, documenting its people and landscapes: this subtly dignified portrait was taken in Canton. The Wellcome Library has 700 of Thomson's glass negatives, most of them taken in China, Taiwan, Cambodia and Thailand.

The Chimu people of northern Peru seated corpses upright, wrapped them in 'mummy bundles' and, like many other cultures, buried them with grave goods. This mummified male body is between 600 and 800 years old.

Understanding the body

What people think they are

Like Wellcome's original collection, which spilled over from the history of medicine into anthropology and the human condition in general, this part of *Medicine Man* overflows its boundaries. Besides objects that depict different ways of understanding the body, such as a Chinese acupuncture figure marked with the energy paths said to underlie the treatment, and a skull mapped into sections according to the doctrines of phrenology, there are objects designed to cause pain, objects used to heal wounds, and figures intended to channel spiritual power. As a whole they attest to the variety

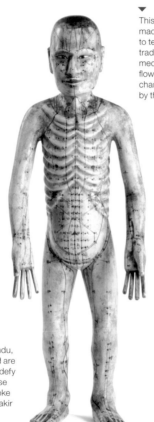

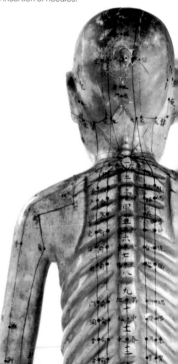

This 17th-century Japanese figure, made from papier-mâché, was used to teach acupuncture. According to traditional Chinese and Japanese medicine, health depends on the flow of energy through the body in channels that can be stimulated by the insertion of needles.

Fakirs are religious devotees, Muslim or Hindu, who live by begging and are famed for being able to defy discomfort or pain. These spike-soled sandals evoke the popular image of a fakir lying on a bed of nails.

Sioux amulet in the shape of a turtle, said to contain a girl's umbilical cord and worn to protect her against illness. Northern Plains, USA, late 19th or early 20th century.

▶
Radiographic image of a nine-month-old fetus, injected to reveal the arteries, 1908.

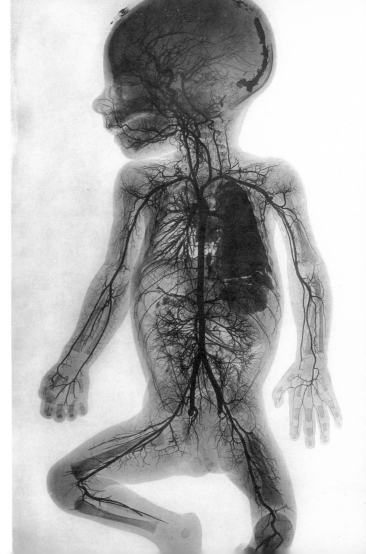

of ways in which the body is understood, and the lengths to which the human imagination can stretch in doing so.

At the same time they underline how widely people have shared certain ideas about the body and the world, or found their own ways to similar views. Belief in spiritual realms, as expressed in a Congolese nkisi figure or a statue of St Michael, is fundamental to cultures everywhere. All around the world people clasp amulets for protection or good fortune.

Perhaps the most extraordinary example is that of trepanning or trephining: making holes

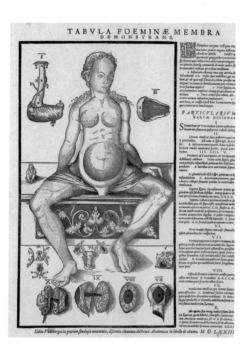

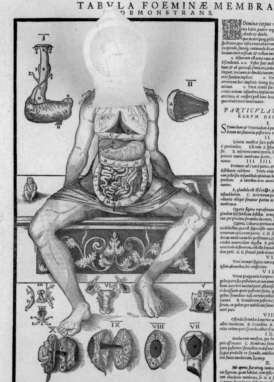

in the skull. People in Asia, Europe, north Africa, Australia, the Pacific and the Americas underwent this primitive surgical procedure, from Neolithic times onwards. A surprisingly high proportion of them survived, some to undergo it again – including one person whose skull was unearthed in Jericho after 4000 years, exposing its cluster of three neatly drilled holes once more. ⓦ

'Fugitive sheets' illustrated anatomy using flaps that could be lifted to reveal images of the body's interior. Wittenberg, 16th century.

This 18th-century model loosely resembles Rembrandt's 1632 painting 'The Anatomy Lesson of Dr Nicolaes Tulp', but with the corpse of an executed criminal replaced by that of a young woman.

Daniel Lambert's size made him a celebrity in the 1800s: he put himself on show, charging a shilling for admission. He died at the age of 39; his tombstone recorded his weight as 52 stone 11 lbs (335 kg).

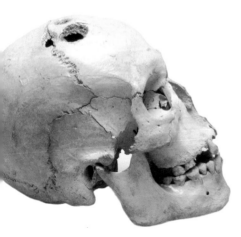

Trepanned skull from Jericho, 2200–2000 BCE.

Model skulls made of ivory, silver and wood.

◄

Jacques-Fabien Gautier d'Agoty shocked 18th-century French viewers with anatomical illustrations that presented figures in classical poses, but with sections of skin and flesh removed.

▶

The English photographer Eadweard Muybridge anatomised the sequences of bodily movement in the 781 plates of his *Animal Locomotion: An electro-photographic investigation of connective phases of animal movements*, published in 1887.

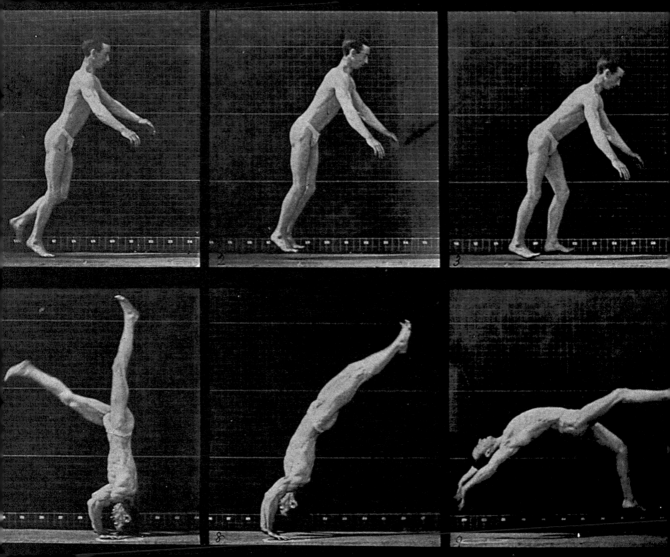

Seeking help

Higher powers, including doctors

People seek medical help from higher powers. They look to gods, spirits, saints, ancestors or magical forces. From the Middle Ages to the 19th century, people in England and France hoped that their monarch's touch would cure scrofula or the 'King's Evil', a form of tuberculosis. As the healing power was believed to be transmissible via objects, 'touchpieces' and lodestones (pieces of magnetite) spared monarchs the need to touch their subjects directly.

Nowadays people also look to medical authority. Stethoscopes, introduced in the 19th century, symbolise the doctor's profession and represent the development of medicine based on empirical observation. But even when scientific medicine is available, people still seek supernatural remedies. Edwardian doctors would listen through their stethoscopes for the sounds of bronchitis; their patients would wear amulets to cure it.

At the same time, much of the help people seek has always involved simple, practical procedures – such as pulling teeth or administering enemas – rather than magic. The universal need for dentistry is all too powerfully expressed by the Chinese doctor's sign hung with strings of teeth, offering a tally of the patients' agonies and the doctor's experience in extractions.

Some procedures, however, were simple but not practical. Bloodletting was based on the doctrine that health depended on a balance in the body between the four 'humours' of blood, black bile, yellow bile and phlegm; recommended by the physician Galen in the second century CE, this practice did not fall from favour until the 19th century. Ⓦ

▶
Portrait of Dr Gachet, Vincent van Gogh's only etching. Paul-Ferdinand Gachet was an unorthodox medical practitioner and art lover who painted, befriended artists, and used electrical apparatus to treat 'melancholia'. He and van Gogh met in May 1890, two months before the artist shot himself. Van Gogh thought Gachet was "sicker than I am".

▶
These amulets, and the brooch above, are from collections acquired by Henry Wellcome and later transferred to the Pitt Rivers Museum, Oxford.

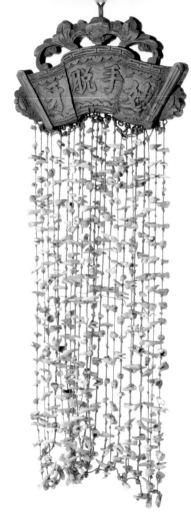

Chinese doctor's signboard, hung with teeth.

The Virgin of Guadalupe, 'Mother of the Americas' and 'Queen of Mexico', who is said to have appeared outside Mexico City in 1531.

Enema syringes were used to get drugs into the body. They were superseded by hypodermic syringes, which were introduced in the mid-19th century.

Kareau figures would be placed outside sick people's houses in the Nicobar Islands, in the eastern Indian Ocean, to scare away the spirits thought to be causing the illness.

Queen Anne, who reigned from 1702 to 1714, is said to have used a lodestone to pass her royal healing power to her subjects without actually having to touch them. (Its silver casing was added by a subsequent owner.)

Scarificator used for bloodletting. English, 19th century.

Chinese women used diagnostic dolls to indicate their symptoms to doctors, as codes of propriety barred medical men from examining female patients directly. This example is ivory and may date from the 18th century.

" I urge **sentient beings** to light **lamps,** make **banners,** liberate **animals** and cultivate **merits** in order to **avoid suffering** and misfortune."

Sutra of the Medicine Buddha (from a 650 CE translation)

A 19th-century Japanese domestic shrine containing figures of 66 Shinto and Buddhist gods, to whom worshippers looked for health and good fortune.

Treating yourself

Medication, consumption, image and identity

Treating yourself can mean all sorts of things: self-medication, sensual pleasure, personal hygiene, grooming, adornment, the art of projecting one's identity. These shade into each other: spectacles correct vision and also adorn the face; cleaning teeth is both hygienic and has a cosmetic effect. Mood-altering substances may be consumed for strictly medicinal purposes, but as the grandiose snuff container shown on p. 59 suggests, their consumption may also be what used to be known as 'luxurious' (and is now more blandly termed 'recreational'). Meanwhile, objects such as corsets and shoes for bound feet remind us that identities are often imposed upon individuals, sometimes by social pressure and sometimes by force.

Objects used for self-care are often embellished in ways that affirm their owners' self-images. A razor owned by the British admiral Horatio Nelson is engraved with hunting scenes, as is an Inuit case used to contain snow goggles.

People may not take good care of themselves if their fortunes don't sustain their self-images, though. Napoleon Bonaparte became Europe's most powerful ruler in the early 19th century, but after a series of military reverses

◀ Plaster cast of the face of Tauque Te Whanoa, 1851, showing Maori tattoos, cut into the skin with a chisel and coloured with soot.

▶ A walking-stick, made of whalebone and ivory, that belonged to Charles Darwin.

▲ These Chinese shoes for bound feet were made in the last decades of the practice, which involved breaking girls' toes and pressing them backwards; it was banned in 1911.

▶ A 'witch doctor' taking snuff; South Africa, early 20th century. This is one of around 6000 photographs documenting black South African culture taken by Alfred Duggan-Cronin.

– in which Nelson played a celebrated part – he ended his life in enforced exile on the south Atlantic island of St Helena. His elegant silver-gilt toothbrush tells one story, but the doctor who attended him at the end of his life told quite another: so much tartar had built up in the former emperor's mouth that his teeth had become detached from their sockets. ⓦ

The Indexo toothbrush, produced in New York in the early 20th century, was designed to fit on the index finger.

A Burroughs Wellcome 'Tabloid' medicine chest taken on the 1933 Mount Everest expedition led by Hugh Ruttledge.

Sir Hiram Maxim called his chest inhaler a Pipe of Peace, but his name was indelibly associated with war: Maxim machine guns, the first automatic weapons, were used to devastating effect by British forces in Africa.

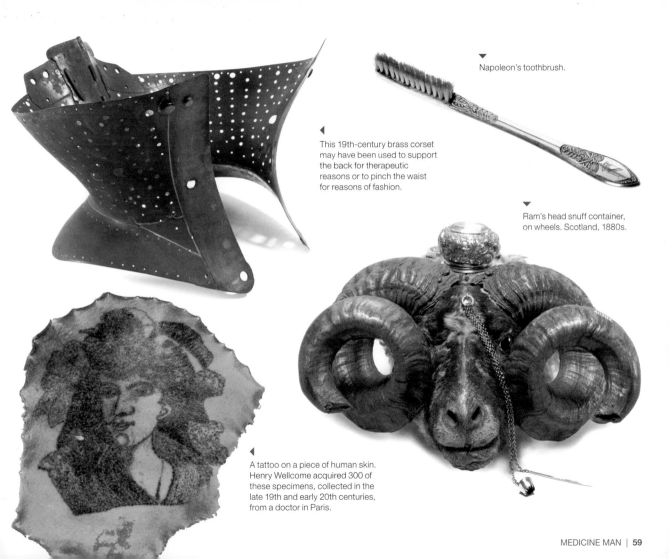

Napoleon's toothbrush.

This 19th-century brass corset may have been used to support the back for therapeutic reasons or to pinch the waist for reasons of fashion.

Ram's head snuff container, on wheels. Scotland, 1880s.

A tattoo on a piece of human skin. Henry Wellcome acquired 300 of these specimens, collected in the late 19th and early 20th centuries, from a doctor in Paris.

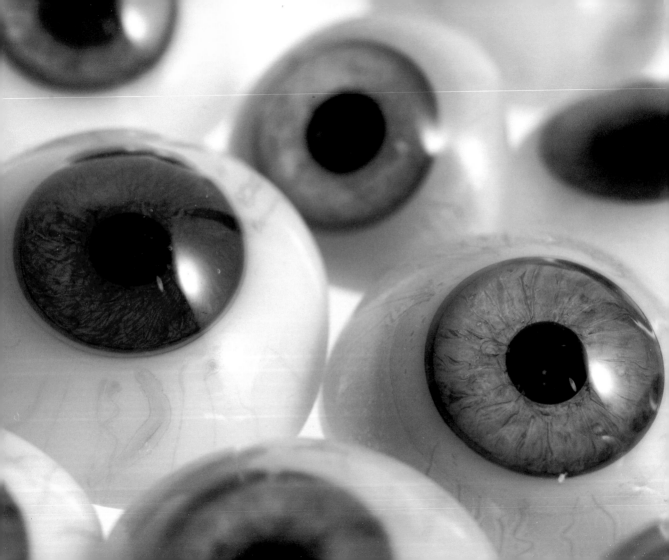

Glass eyes: minutely detailed, varied, lifelike and fragile. These may date from around 1900.

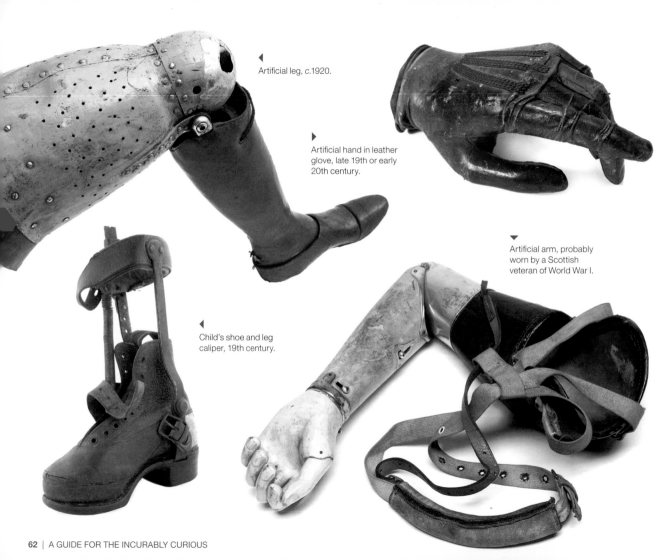

Artificial leg, *c*.1920.

Artificial hand in leather glove, late 19th or early 20th century.

Artificial arm, probably worn by a Scottish veteran of World War I.

Child's shoe and leg caliper, 19th century.

▶
This wooden leg dates
from the early 20th century
but is of a type known as
the 'Anglesey leg', after
one worn by the Marquis
of Anglesey to replace the
limb he lost at the Battle
of Waterloo in 1815.

" ... my tank was hit, **on fire**, and I saw
my hands were **blown off.** I sat back
in my seat and determined **'This is the end'**
... And then, I had always kept a photograph of **my
wife** pasted up in front of me, and **I saw her**,
and I knew that **no matter** how I came back,
that's what she would **want.**"

Jim Toft, British serviceman, wounded in action 30 October 1940

◀
Steel hand and forearm
with leather arm socket,
late 19th century.

Medicine
Now

10 10 10 11 11 11 11 11 12 12

13 14 14 14 14 15 15 15 15 16

18 18 18 19 19 19 20 20 20 21

X X X Y Y Y

Medicine has been transformed by biomedical advances, economic growth and social change in the decades since the Wellcome Trust came into existence. Prosperity and antibiotics have shrunk the burden of infectious disease in high-income countries, shifting the weight of concern from childhood illnesses to those of later life. Computing power has enabled medicine to map, image and monitor the body to ever-finer degrees of resolution. Human genomes, three billion units long, can be sequenced and surveyed.

The benefits have not been evenly spread, however. Millions of children die each year in low-income countries from diarrhoea, pneumonia, malaria and other infectious diseases. Because malaria imposes a huge burden on Africa in particular, the disease has come to represent the gap between the health of rich and poor nations. The morbid consequences of plenty in rich countries are represented by obesity – though it tends to affect poorer people in generally wealthy societies, and is not confined to these countries.

Obesity also takes us to the heart of the intimate relationship in modern Western societies between wellbeing, body image, emotions and identity. The control of body weight is seen to be not only the basis of health and attractiveness but also a telling indicator of efficiency and self-discipline. Doctors and health agencies urge people to take care of themselves, but many cannot live up to the standards medicine and society now expect of them.

Telling people to take care of themselves does, however, encourage the prevalent feeling that even as patients they should not be passive. People seek out new ways to take the initiative in their own healthcare. Few are more radical than Michael Landy's painfully clear drawing of his genitals after the removal of a testicle. It conveys a determination to rebuild his relationship with his body, and not to leave the task solely to the doctors. ⓦ

As displays are changed periodically, the objects featured in these pages may not all correspond exactly to what is on show in the galleries at any one time.

The body

New ways of understanding anatomy

In 1938, two years after Henry Wellcome's death, a team of physicists led by Isidor Isaac Rabi developed a method for measuring the magnetic resonance of atoms. Half a century later, magnetic resonance technology brought a new kind of life to images of the living body, lighting it in all the colours of the spectrum instead of the pale shadows cast by X-rays. Rabi lived just long enough to undergo an MRI scan himself, shortly before his death in 1988.

Today doctors can use a range of techniques to see inside the body without cutting it open, creating virtual images of their patients. The moment when a woman feels her baby first move in the womb is supplemented by ultrasound scans that allow her to see her baby's body in motion. Cells and their contents are illuminated by

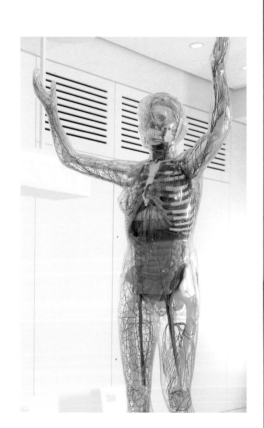

▶
Transparent female anatomical model, c.1980.

> **"** It was **eerie.** I saw **myself** in that **machine.** I never thought my **work** would come to this."
>
> **Isidor Isaac Rabi (1898–1988)**

electron microscopy: biomedical images portray bacteria lurking within tissue like animals in the forests depicted in old paintings.

Like paintings, modern biomedical images draw upon a palette of artificial colours. Much of the impact of MRI images comes from the intensity and contrast of the colours selected to generate them. While artists have been intrigued by these new ways to construct images, they aspire to subtlety rather than spectacle, and they may look at the new images with a critical eye. Luke Jerram, for example, created a clear glass sculpture of the human immunodeficiency virus "in response to the constant bombardment by coloured images we receive through the media". ⓦ

▲ In Annie Cattrell's 'SENSE' series (2001–03), fMRI scans of a brain responding to stimuli from the five senses were turned into three-dimensional amber resin forms.

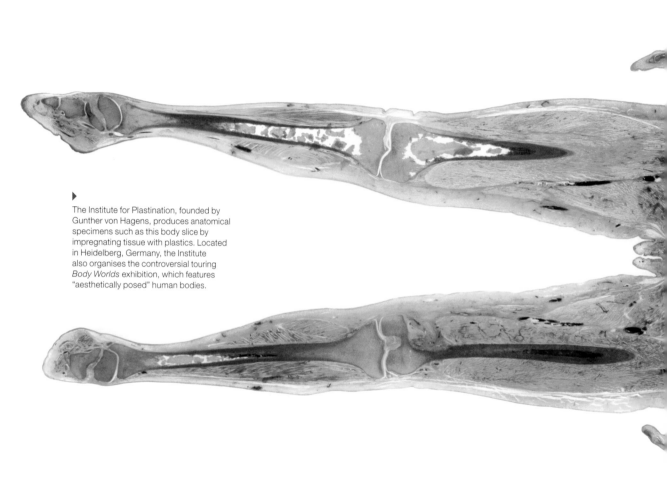

The Institute for Plastination, founded by Gunther von Hagens, produces anatomical specimens such as this body slice by impregnating tissue with plastics. Located in Heidelberg, Germany, the Institute also organises the controversial touring *Body Worlds* exhibition, which features "aesthetically posed" human bodies.

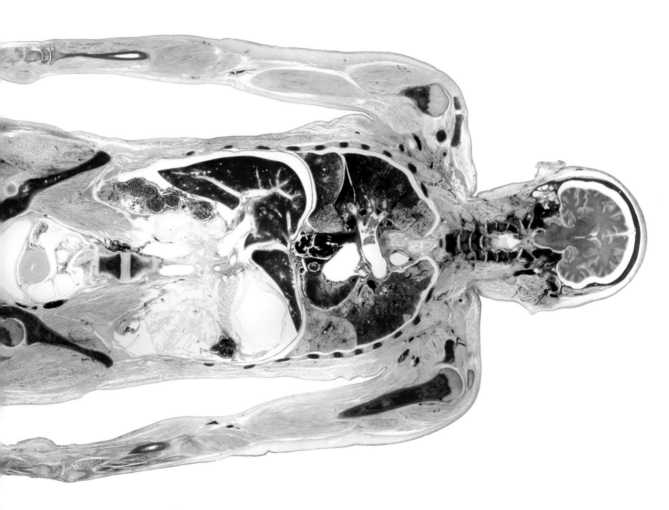

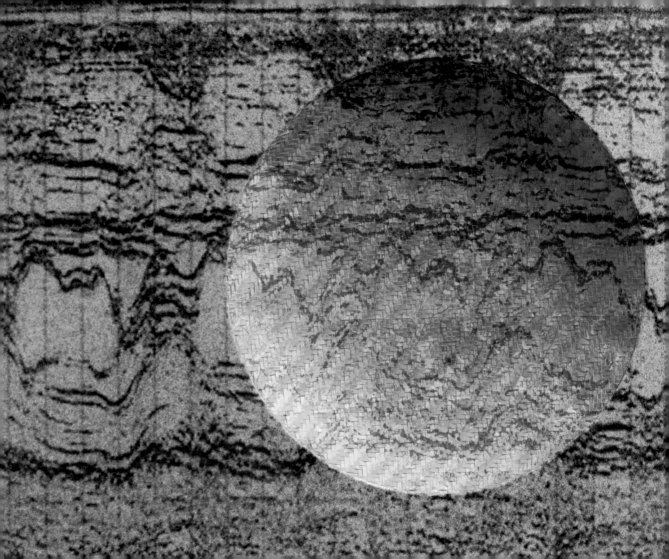

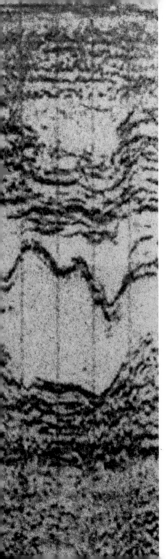

◄

In 'Rockies/Karakoram',
by Chris Drury (2003), maps
of the two mountain ranges
are woven together with an
echocardiogram image of
the heart.

▶

'Swine Flu' by Luke Jerram,
2009, shows the structure
of the H1N1 virus.

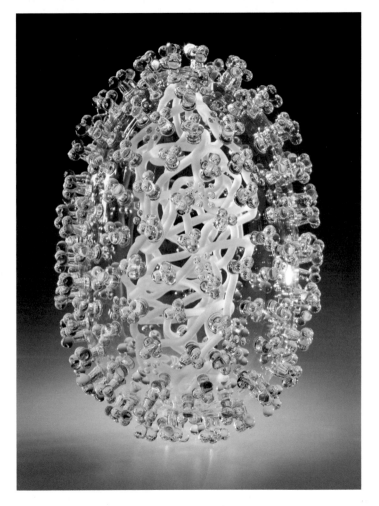

Genomes

The consequences of sequencing

Medicine, science and society have entered the genomic era, in which entire genetic code sequences for species and individuals can be catalogued. Genomics can shed light on the evolution of species, the history of population movements and the prospects for an individual's health. It encourages visions of 'personalised medicine', in which each person's care is tailored to their particular combination of genes, but also arouses fears about discrimination and privacy. The more knowledge biomedical science offers people about their genetic make-up, the more difficult their choices will become, about what they should find out and how they should respond.

The first great human genome sequencing project – in which the Wellcome Trust-funded Sanger Centre under the direction of John Sulston played a major part – delivered its results in the first years of this century. Scientists, artists and society at large

have responded to such achievements with awe, curiosity, uncertainty and unease.

One of the challenges they all face is to find metaphors to represent the new data. The four letters that represent the units of the genetic code – G, A, T, C – prompt the idea that a genome is a kind of text, a 'book of life' or a library. But although it's an intuitive image, it sits uncomfortably with the sense that an individual is more than just a sequence of code. Andrea Duncan's artwork '23 Pairs' brings out the humanity in genetic information by playing on the visual similarity between chromosomes and odd socks, giving a homely feel to a laboratory array. ⬤

◀ Mauro Perruchetti's 'Jelly Baby 3' (2004) is a metaphor for human cloning.

▶ Daniel Lee's 'Origin' (1999–2003) uses digital morphing techniques to tell a Darwinian story about how living forms evolve from one to another.

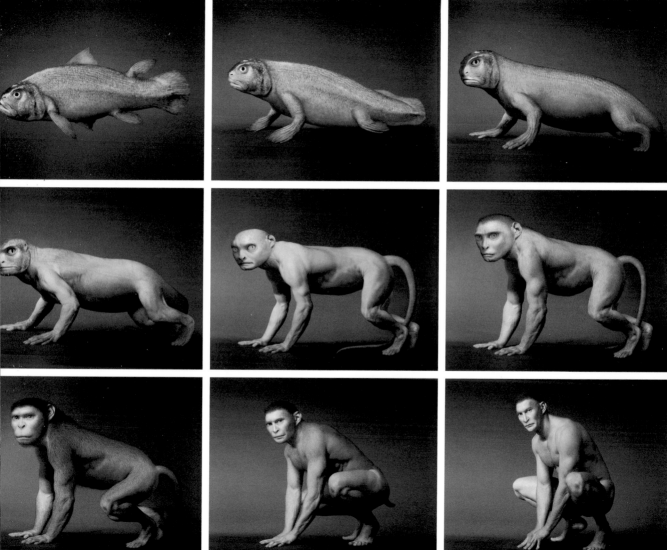

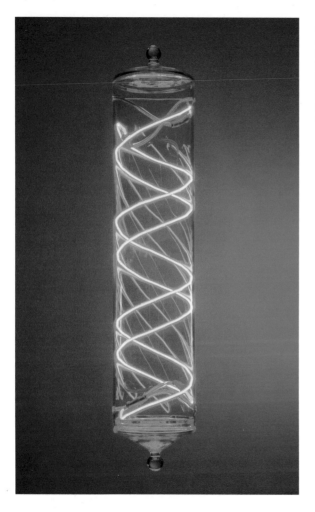

'Barber DNA', by Robin Blackledge (2003), links the image of the barber's sign pole, said to be derived from bloodstained bandages displayed outside barber-surgeons' premises, with the spiral form of the DNA molecule.

Rob Kesseler's 'Bud' (2002) reflects on the potential benefits and dangers of genetic modification. Kesseler presents this container of genetically modified soybeans "as both a trophy and time bomb".

> ## " We are standing at a watershed between **observation** in **biology** and **creation**."
>
> Sir John Sulston (b. 1942)

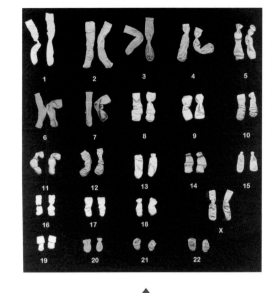

Andrea Duncan's '23 Pairs' (2002): socks arranged in the karyotype format used to represent the chromosomes of a cell.

'Anagram', by Julie Cockburn (2005), responds to the Human Genome Project and is made up of letters representing the four base molecules of the genetic code. It also includes words like 'joy' and 'heaven', as reminders that the data are human.

Obesity

The modern world's disease

Humans are rapidly becoming an urban species. More than half the world's population now lives in cities and towns; the proportion is projected to reach 70 per cent by the middle of the century. When people move into cities, their ways of life change. Buying their food rather than growing it, they eat more fat and sugar; many of them become less physically active. Obesity levels are rising as a result, and disease associated with excessive weight is now believed to kill around three million people a year.

In high-income countries, excessive weight has become a major concern for public health authorities and a preoccupation for millions of individuals. Obesity symbolises the contradictions within societies that promote consumption by marketing pleasurable sensations but also demand that individuals discipline themselves to be healthy and look good. While medicine and official agencies view obesity as a health crisis, popular attitudes still reveal a moralistic tendency to see it as the consequence of greed.

'I Can't Help the Way I Feel', by John Isaacs (2003). Isaacs suggests that "the way in which the flesh grows, erupts and engulfs the body can be seen as a metaphor of the way in which we become incapacitated by the emotional landscape in which we live and over which we have little control".

No consumption without documentation: under the rules Ellie Harrison set herself for 'Eat 22' (2001–02) she had to photograph all the food she ate, including "wherever possible all handfuls" of party food, and eat all the food she photographed.

The challenges are powerfully expressed by John Isaacs's anti-heroic monument to obesity, 'I Can't Help the Way I Feel', and by Ellie Harrison's 'Eat 22' project, an exercise in dietary discipline that required her to photograph everything she ate from her 22nd birthday to her 23rd. Both portray burdens borne by individuals – a loss of control in one case, an excess of control in the other – and highlight, in Isaacs's words, "the plight of the individual" in contemporary society.

Malaria

An international cause

More than half a century after the World Health Organization launched its Global Malaria Eradication Program in 1955, hundreds of millions of people still fall ill with the disease each year, and many hundreds of thousands die as a result. The world abandoned the goal of eradicating malaria in 1969, and cases increased as the parasites evolved resistance to drugs.

The campaign against malaria has regained the initiative, though. The Roll Back Malaria Partnership, which has coordinated international efforts since 1998, has overseen a decline in mortality of 25 per cent. Eradication has re-emerged as the ultimate goal.

Progress has been made through commitment, funding, insecticide and mosquito nets. When infection is not prevented, it can be treated with artemisinin, which comes from a plant used in traditional Chinese medicine to treat fevers. Chinese researchers reported its antimalarial action in 1979; the report was noticed and followed up by Nick White and his colleagues in the Wellcome Trust research unit at Mahidol University in Bangkok.

Efforts to control the disease are concentrated in sub-Saharan Africa, where 90 per cent of malarial deaths occur – a large proportion of them in children under five. The campaign's profile in high-income countries has been raised by the involvement of the software entrepreneur and philanthropist Bill Gates, who insists that as a matter of moral duty, malaria must be not just controlled but extirpated altogether. His ambition would surely have impressed Henry Wellcome, another entrepreneur and philanthropist who funded efforts to control malaria.

In Alastair Mackie's 'Mosquito Coast' (2002), the world's coastlines are made up of dead mosquitoes. Malaria's global prevalence has in fact diminished markedly since 2000: of 99 countries in which malaria is transmitted, 43 recorded that, by 2010, the number of cases had fallen by more than half.

"My children will not die from malaria, **thank God.** Since that is true, **no child** should die."

Bill Gates (b. 1955)

Living with medical science

Patients take the initiative

Medicine's relationships with the people it treats have changed as fast as its science in recent decades. Patients play increasingly active roles in their treatment, and are less awed by doctors than they once were. They seek out information about their conditions; they sometimes consider alternative treatments; they may join others who share their condition to form self-help communities; and they are often ready to challenge insensitive or dismissive attitudes in those around them.

These changes are part of broader shifts in society, in which deference to authority has declined, while deference to consumer choice has increased. They are also the product of activism, particularly around AIDS in the 1980s, when dissatisfaction with medical responses to the epidemic helped to stimulate a re-evaluation of the relationships that develop around illness.

More recently the internet has given people access to medical information that was previously the preserve of experts. Patients may now be better informed about their conditions than their general practitioners, who don't have the time to read the latest specialist research papers – or they may be encouraged to reject orthodox medicine in favour of alternative doctrines promoted online.

In these questioning, demanding, self-conscious times, people are preoccupied with their own experiences of illness and wellbeing. The materials in the gallery illustrating the experiences of doctors, scientists and patients affirm the importance of understanding different perspectives on medicine, knowledge and health. ⓦ

▲

'Collection: Acts of Faith' by Julian Walker (2003). In this work, non-prescription tablets, vitamins and herbal supplements have been carved into images of those parts of the body that they are designed to treat. The artist draws on the tradition of ex-voto objects as well as the medieval doctrine that the medical efficacy of a substance was based on its resemblance to particular body parts.

▶
The repeating motif "This should not be difficult" is etched on the base of 'Dyslexia' (2004). Artist Katharine Dowson explains that it is "the whisper that follows dyslexic children by well-meaning teachers or parents not understanding the frustrations dyslexic children feel".

'After Image' (1997) is a series of 24 photographs by Alexa Wright in which their subjects' phantom limbs have been visualised.

'Left-Sided Orchidectomy II', Michael Landy (2005).

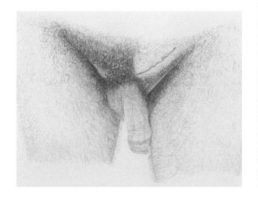

Wellcome
Library

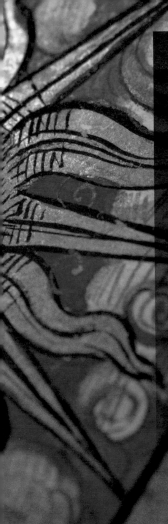

The Library was the first part of Henry Wellcome's collection and today it is the largest. Although the museum objects outnumbered the Library holdings two to one by the time he died, the Library's catalogue now outnumbers the museum inventory by about 25 to one. In 1936 the Library was thought to contain half a million items. Now there are 2.5 million, with the catalogue still growing.

Nearly a million of the items are books; a quarter of a million are visual materials – paintings, prints, photographs, moving images – and the bulk of the remainder is archives and manuscripts. The catalogue ranges from an ancient Egyptian medical prescription written on papyrus to the digitally processed modern biomedical images that illuminate the fabric of nature.

Like Wellcome's objects, his library reveals a roving gaze. His first major purchases, in 1898, were from the library of the artist

A richly illuminated manuscript of Pierre Boaistuau's book *Histoires Prodigieuses*, featuring "monsters, prodigies and abominations", which was prepared for presentation to Queen Elizabeth I in 1560.

William Morris; their interest lay mainly in typography and design. Among the subsequent acquisitions were a Burmese Buddhist manuscript made from a king's silk robe, an 18th-century Venetian Jewish marriage contract, and the Persian prince Iskandar's horoscope, bought for £6 15s at a Sotheby's auction.

Today the Library's collections make it a formidable resource, encompassing the history of medicine and indeed all aspects of the broader history of health. Digitisation is enabling it to make its diversity more accessible: Wellcome Images, the free online picture library, sums up its offering as "2000 years of human culture".

The online texts include a 1543 textbook by the great anatomist Vesalius, 18th-century pamphlets about a woman said to have given birth to rabbits, and a handwritten remedy book, dated 1692, that became the library's first recorded acquisition in 1897. More recently, the Library has found room on its shelves for the autobiography of the Rolling Stones guitarist Keith Richards, who in his own way has earned a footnote in the history of health.

People and places

Travellers' tales and trophies

Henry Wellcome was a pioneer and a traveller from the start. He was raised in frontier country as America expanded west, and as a young man he worked for a pharmaceutical company journeying through Ecuador and Peru in search of cinchona bark, the source of the antimalarial drug quinine. He had an expeditionary spirit: when he became a pharmaceutical tycoon, he used his success to add explorers such as Henry Morton Stanley to his circle of acquaintances.

When he began to collect for his museum and library, his reach – extended by the agents he employed – became global. The archives preserve his correspondence with his agents, from the scrupulously diplomatic Paira Mall to the colourful raconteur Captain Peter Johnston-Saint. Wellcome himself still enjoyed the thrill of the quest and the unmade road, to his wife Syrie's increasing frustration.

He was part of the broader movement of the colonial age, seeking out valuables in poorer

▶ Bodybuilders of the Physical Culture Society of Montreal, 1905.

▶ Peruvian woman and llama, by Sir Clements Robert Markham, geographer, 1853.

◀ Japanese actor, by Kunisada, 1861.

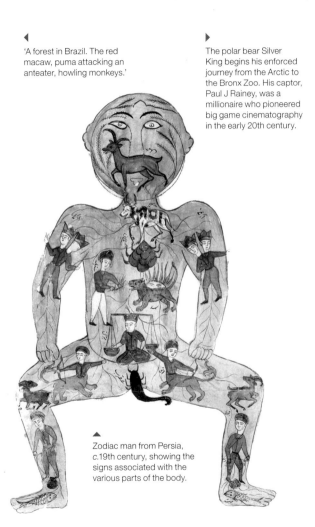

'A forest in Brazil. The red macaw, puma attacking an anteater, howling monkeys.'

The polar bear Silver King begins his enforced journey from the Arctic to the Bronx Zoo. His captor, Paul J Rainey, was a millionaire who pioneered big game cinematography in the early 20th century.

Zodiac man from Persia, *c.*19th century, showing the signs associated with the various parts of the body.

regions and adding them to the wealth of rich nations. The relationships that formed between Europeans and people of distant cultures in the process were often as complex as they were unequal.

Many European travellers recorded their experiences and impressions in journals and sketchbooks. The naval surgeons, naturalists, explorers and tourists who compiled these documents also told of long sea voyages, desolate landscapes and strange wildlife. Not all survived to finish their tales: in 1871, Charles Hall wrote a letter from near the spot on the Greenland coast he called Thank God Harbour, shortly before falling fatally ill and accusing his officers of murdering him. ⓦ

Two water snakes swallow a fish and a frog. According to historian A K Coomaraswamy, this illustrates the Bengali spiritual teaching that "it is harder to escape from debauchery once you have taken to it than it is for a fish to escape alive from the mouth of a snake".

Horoscope from south-west Iran showing the heavens at the time of the birth of Iskandar Sultan, a grandson of the Central Asian conqueror Timur, or Tamerlane, on 25 April 1384. Written in 1411, it predicts a long and successful life. In the event, Iskandar was executed in 1415 after being defeated in family power struggles, during which he was blinded by one of his brothers.

The brain and the mind

Getting inside our heads

Although neuroscientists can now turn thinking into a digital light-show by the use of scanners, the 17th-century anatomist Thomas Willis's suggestion that the brain is capable of understanding everything but itself still has a ring of truth. Human neuroscience studies the most complex known object, its researches adding steadily to the complexity that is known.

Phrenology, with its grandiose lexicon of traits like 'amativeness' and 'credenciveness', made it sound beguilingly easy: the texture of the mind derived from the shape of the brain, which could be discerned from the shape of the head. The study of the brain and the study of the mind have been largely separate projects, however.

The Library's archives document the work of many important figures in the history of psychology and psychiatry. They include the papers of Charles Spearman (part of the British Psychological Society collection),

whose notion of general intelligence underlies IQ testing and the angry controversies over the extent to which intelligence is heritable. Also represented are the child psychoanalyst Melanie Klein, and her one-time trainee John Bowlby, who moved from psychoanalysis towards biology in developing his theory about how infants form attachments to parents or other carers.

▼
Dissections of the brain and blood vessels, by Jacques-Fabien Gautier d'Agoty, 1748.

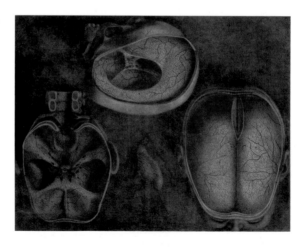

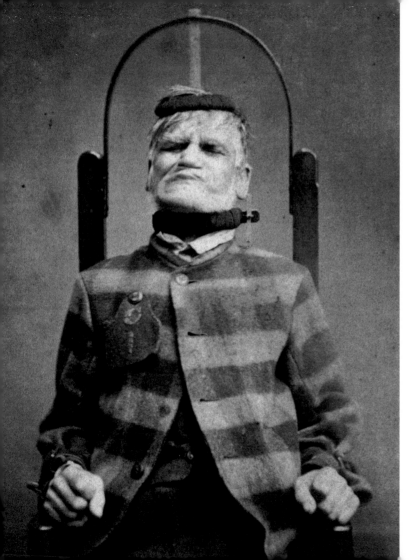

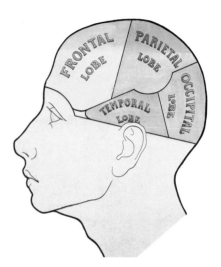

◀ A mentally ill man strapped into a restraint chair in Wakefield Prison, Yorkshire, 1869.

▲ A drawing made around the turn of the 20th century by Bernard Hollander, a psychiatrist who tried to reinvent the phrenological ideas that had been developed by Franz Joseph Gall nearly a century earlier.

Disorders of the mind have proved as hard to understand as the brain's orderly functioning. Records from lunatic asylums are among the documents that illustrate changing responses to mental illness. They include inmates' drawings and letters, such as one, from 1896, in which the writer says she is being killed by the steady removal of parts of her body. ⓦ

> ❝ ... to explicate the uses of the Brain, seems as **difficult a task** as to **paint the Soul,** of which it is commonly said, That it understands all things but it self ...❞
>
> **Thomas Willis (1621–1675)**

▲
These photographs were taken around 1869 at the West Riding Lunatic Asylum. The man on the left was diagnosed with "monomania of pride"; the one in the middle with "melancholia"; and the image on the right was labelled "organic dementia".

▶
Drawing by 'Richard', one of Melanie Klein's child patients, 1941.

The Hospital of Bethlehem at Moorfields, London, *c*.1750. Founded in 1247, it began to treat mental illness in the 14th century. In 1770 it was closed to the sightseers who knew it as Bedlam.

An inmate of the Craiglockhart Workhouse, aged 82, diagnosed with senile dementia, 1896. "His sight and hearing were dull, he took little notice of his surroundings, spoke little, and seldom responded to questions," the physician Sir Byrom Bramwell observed.

Honoré Daumier caricatures 'animal magnetism' and public gullibility. The 'magnetiser' claims that his subject will give medical advice and reveal the location of buried treasure in her sleep. Paris, 1838.

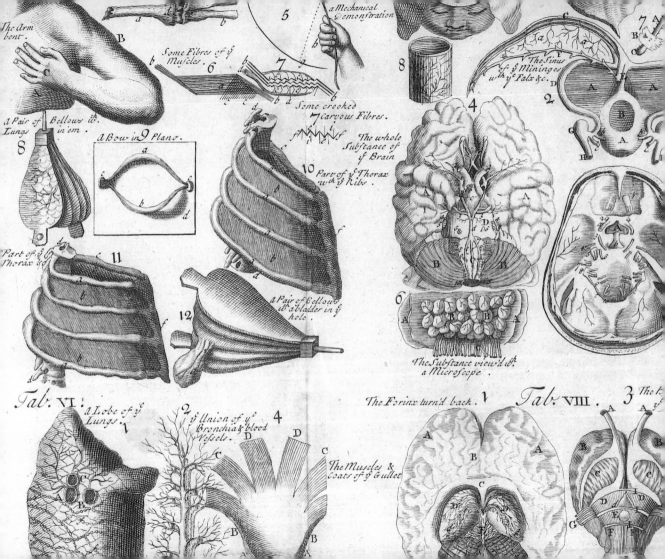

The Arm bent.

B

a   b   5

a Mechanical Demonstration

b   g

8

7

C

The Sinus of ye Mininges with ye Falx &c.

2

B   E   F

G

H   A

a   b

Some Fibres of ye Muscles. 6

b   a   7

Some crooked carvous Fibres.

The whole Substance of ye Brain

a Pair of Bellows ye Lungs in 'em.

8

a Bow in 9 Plano.

a

c   e

b   d

10

Part of ye Thorax with ye Ribs

4

A   A

D

B   B   B

Part of ye Thorax &c.

11

12

a Pair of Bellows ye a bladder in ye hole.

6

A   B   A

The Substance view'd ye a Microscope.

Tab. VI.

a Lobe of ye Lungs. 1

2 ye Union of ye Bronchia & blood Vessels.

4

D

C   D

C

The Muscles & Coats of ye Gullet

A

C

C

B

The Forinx turn'd back. 1

A   A

B

Tab. VIII.

3

The

A   A

A

B   B   B

B

C   C

D   D

E

F

G   F

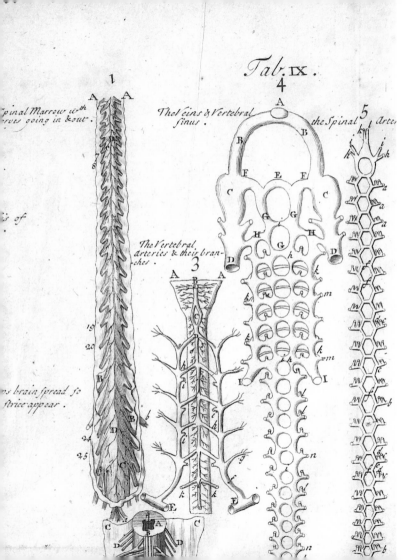

Tab. IX.

pinal Marrow with
rves going in & out.

The Veins & Vertebral
sinus.

the Spinal Arter.

The Vertebral
arteries & their bran-
ches.

s of

s brain spread so
trice appear.

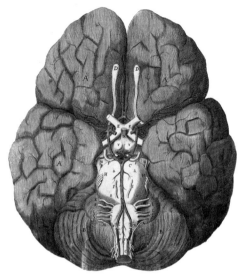

◀ Brains among the
structures illustrated in
the *Bibliotheca Anatomica,
Medica, Chirurgica &c.*,
written by medical experts
and issued in monthly parts,
1711–14.

▲ Brain drawn for Thomas
Willis's *Cerebri anatome*,
1664, by Sir Christopher
Wren, whom Willis affirmed
was "frequently present at
our Dissection, to confer
and reason out the use
of the Parts".

Public health

Sanitation, exhortation and education

Dr John Snow's map shows that cholera deaths in 1854 Soho were clustered around one particular water pump. It also shows how public health works: gathering information, making connections between the conditions of people's lives and their health, and finding ways to convey the resulting messages that make them healthier.

Snow conveyed his message to local officials, who had the pump handle removed. Nowadays, with sanitary conditions established in high-income countries through investment, regulation and monitoring, public authorities devote immense effort to sending people messages about how they can protect their health by adapting their

> **Within two hundred and fifty yards of the spot where Cambridge Street joins Broad Street there were upwards of five hundred fatal attacks of cholera in ten days. The mortality in this limited area probably equals any that was ever caused in this country, even by the plague ..."**
> **John Snow (1813–1858)**

Map showing deaths from cholera in Broad Street and neighbouring parts of Soho from 19 August to 30 September 1854, by Dr John Snow, *On the Mode of Communication of Cholera*, 1855.

United States Public Health Service poster urging tests for syphilis, 1940.

SYPHILIS *Strikes* 1 *in* 10 *before* 50

A BLOOD TEST — THE ONLY SURE CHECK

UNITED STATES PUBLIC HEALTH SERVICE

НЕ ПЕЙ СЫРОЙ ВОДЫ

ГРЯЗНАЯ ВОДА И МУХИ РАЗНОСЯТ ЗАРАЗУ

НЕ ЕШЬ СЫРЫХ ФРУКТОВ И БАЗАРНОЙ СТРЯПНИ

БОЛЬНОЙ ЧЕЛОВЕК — ИСТОЧНИК ЗАРАЗЫ

behaviour. Food, tobacco, alcohol and sex are among the most prominent themes.

When the AIDS epidemic emerged in the 1980s, it posed an unprecedented challenge for public health media. A new sexually transmitted infection had appeared during a period in which mores were changing. Traditional approaches to sexual health propaganda, trading on shame and misogyny, had become decreasingly effective and increasingly unacceptable; but at the same time, approaches that affirmed sex, and sexual diversity, faced opposition on traditional moral grounds.

The Wellcome Library's collection of over 3000 AIDS posters spans 99 countries, 75 languages and a range of idioms, through which campaigners have attempted to work with the grain of human nature and its various local cultures. It is a compendium of contemporary identities and how they have evolved in response to a virus. ⓦ

Cartoon promoting condom use, Queensland, Australia, 1990s.

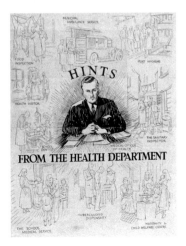

◄ Ukrainian Soviet poster urging people to avoid unhygienic behaviour that spreads cholera, 1921.

◄ Medical Officers of Health were key figures in public health authorities across England and Wales from the 1870s to the 1970s.

Recipes and remedies

Health begins at home

The hands that wrote Lady Ayscough's book seem tireless, their script leaning purposefully forward, and confident, rendering their capitals with extravagant flourishes like the doffing of a gentleman's hat. Over 250 pages are filled with "receits of phisick and chirurgery": medical recipes for a range of conditions including such grave illnesses as consumption (tuberculosis) and the plague. It is a comprehensive manual of medicine compiled within and for the benefit of a single family, documenting the knowledge available at the higher levels of early modern English society.

Lady Ayscough's book was the Library's first documented acquisition and the first of over 270 such volumes, dating from the 16th century to the 19th, to enter the catalogue. They record a period of history in which medicine was part of the domestic knowledge that women organised and transmitted within families. This period was coming to an end by the time Lady

Ayscough's book was written in 1692. Men took over medicine, leaving cookery and other household concerns to women.

The full recipe and remedy sequence spans nearly a millennium, from the Library's oldest European document, an Old English parchment list of folk remedies written around

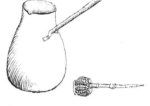

▲
Drawing of a chocolate pot in the margins of Lady Ann Fanshawe's recipe book of receipts (see p. 102).

▼
Among the many diseases Parker's Tonic (1880s) claimed to cure was "blood foul with humours".

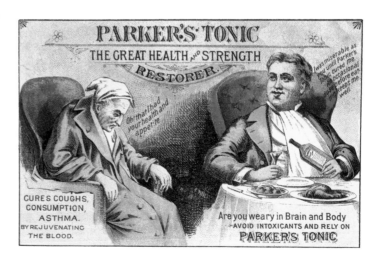

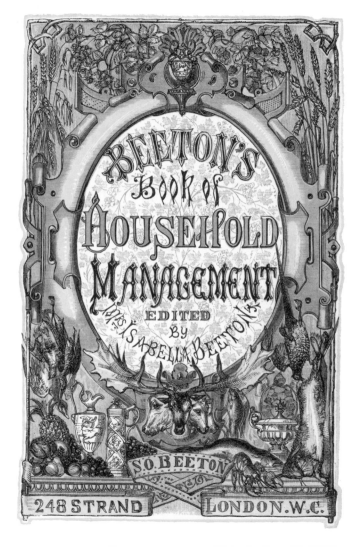

◄

While most of Mrs Isabella Beeton's rigorously organised *Book of Household Management* (1861) is devoted to recipes, it also provides instructions for medical treatment, advice on child-rearing, and details of servants' duties.

1000, to Mrs Beeton's celebrated book of household management, which first appeared in 1861. Isabella Beeton's biographer Kathryn Hughes has reintroduced a medical dimension to the household scene by using a doctor's notes, held by the Library, to support her hunch that Mr Beeton infected his wife with syphilis. Ⓦ

My Mother. ✗   Dr: Burges his Directions in tyme of Plague

A Honshawe Take three pints of Malmsey, boile in it a handfull of Sage
handfull of Rue, till a pinte be wasted, then straine it and sett
it over ye fire againe, and putt thereto a penny worth of long Pepp
halfe an ounce of Ginger, a Quarter of an Ounce of Nutmegs, all
beaten together. then let it boile a little, and take it of the Fire
putt to it 4 pennyworth of Mithridate, 2 pennyworth of Treac
& a quarter of a pint of the best Angelico water. keepe this as yo
Life above all wordly treasure. take it alwaies warme both mornin
and Euening a Spoonfull or two if You be infected, and sweat thereu
but if You be not infected then one spoonefull a day is sufficient, hal
a spoonfull in the morning and halfe at night. In all Your Plague
time under God trust to this. For there was neuer none died of the
Plague that tooke it. This is not only good for the Common Plag
But for the Measells, Small Poxe, Surfetts, and diuers other kine
of Diseases.

To make Lozenges for a Cold.

Jalappa of gialappae, Swarti pruiger Wortel, Wonder bloem van peru

▲

Illustration from a copy of John French's *Art of Distillation*, 1651, which contains a book of medical and cookery receipts by Rebecca Tallamy written in the margins and dated 1735.

◄

Japanese translation of a Dutch herbal by Rembert Dodoens, 17th century.

◄

(Opposite page) Page detailing a plague treatment from Lady Ann Fanshawe's *Booke of Receipts of Physickes, Salves, Waters, Cordialls, Preserves and Cookery*, compiled between 1651 and 1707.

Magic and the occult

Imagining the invisible

Alchemy was far more than the quest to transmute base metals into gold: the stone that alchemists sought was, after all, the philosopher's. Classical medicine was as magical as it was rational; thinkers like the 16th-century physician Paracelsus drew upon the occult until science separated itself out as a distinctive way of knowledge. In the 17th century Isaac Newton was fascinated by alchemy as well as by gravity.

The pursuit of the philosopher's stone is depicted in the Library's two Ripley Scrolls. More than three metres long, they were made in the 17th century and are named after George Ripley, a 15th-century Augustinian canon. The archives also contain an alchemical notebook referring to Ripley's work by John Dee, the Elizabethan astrologer, natural philosopher and mathematician.

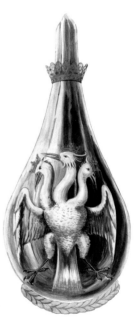

A 15th-century copy of an alchemical text by Raymundus Lullius (Ramon Llull), 13th-century Majorcan thinker.

'Good wizard of the Kakadu tribe sucking evil magic from a sick man,' from *Handbook for Australia*, 1914.

A three-headed eagle in a crowned alchemical flask, representing mercury sublimated (refined) three times. From Salomon Trismosin's 16th-century alchemical treatise *Splendor solis* ('Splendour of the Sun').

Although Ripley combined his vocation with alchemy, ventures into magic held terrors for the faithful, who feared contact with devilish powers. In the late 15th century such fantasies were detailed in the *Malleus Maleficarum* (or *Hexenhammer*, the hammer of witches). This handbook for witch-hunters was compiled by two Dominican inquisitors whom Pope Innocent VIII authorised to find and punish witches in northern Germany. The Library's copy was written in 1494; the book's influence persisted into the 18th century. Portraying witchcraft as the work of women, it answered questions such as whether witches could turn men into beasts, or make their "virile members" seem to disappear. Such questions were frequently asked: tens of thousands were killed in Europe's witch-hunts. ⓦ

John Dee, renowned for the breadth of his natural and supernatural knowledge, was an astrologer to Queen Elizabeth I. He demonstrates a chemical reaction before her in this painting by Henry Gillard Glindoni.

> Many have said of **alchemy** that it is for making **gold** and **silver**. But here such is not the aim but to consider only what virtue and **power** may lie in medicines."

Paracelsus (1493–1541)

Magical mayhem: a ghost appears as a man conducts magic rites and a hunter cowers in terror.

The pursuit of science

Public knowledge and private lives

A scientific paper is an agreed statement, the product of negotiations between authors, referees and editors. Scientists' personal papers cast more light on the politics of the pursuit of science: alliances, rivalries, tensions (creative or otherwise) and the complicated paths that researchers take through the institutions that support them.

Such papers also show that science is a more untidy business than the published work makes it look. Howard Florey, who shared a Nobel Prize with Ernst Chain and Alexander Fleming for their work on penicillin, remarked that "we usually blunder from one lot of dubious observations to another". That may partly explain tensions such as those between the three laureates, and questions such as whether their colleague Norman Heatley should have received more credit than he did. Heatley's and Chain's papers are both held by the Wellcome Library, as are those of Francis Crick, who co-discovered the DNA double helix.

The politics of epidemiology are glimpsed in a letter from Richard Doll, observing that he may need

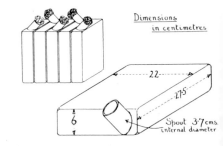

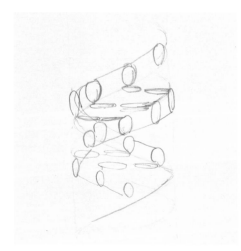

The DNA helix sketched by Francis Crick in 1953, the year that he and James Watson described the molecule's structure.

Professor Sir Harry Kroto, photographed by Anne-Katrin Purkiss behind models of fullerenes, the day after the announcement that he and two colleagues had been awarded the 1996 Nobel Prize in Chemistry for discovering these carbon molecules. Wellcome Image Award winner, 2009.

Apparatus for producing penicillin, sketched by Norman Heatley, one of the biochemists who developed the drug for medical use in the late 1930s and early 1940s.

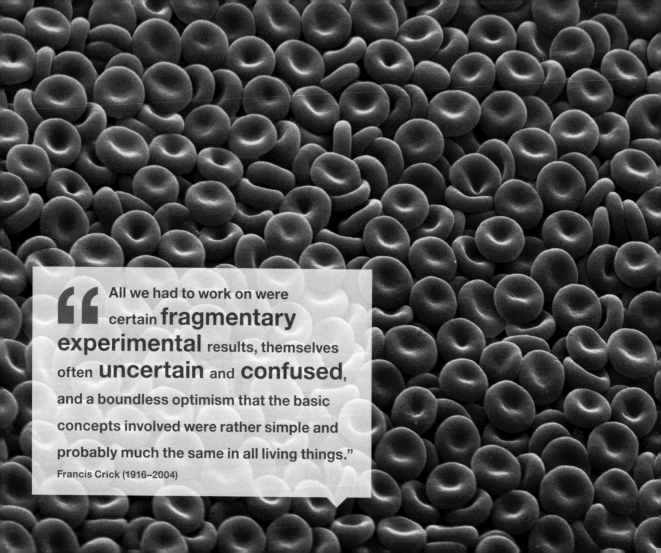

> "All we had to work on were certain **fragmentary experimental** results, themselves often **uncertain** and **confused**, and a boundless optimism that the basic concepts involved were rather simple and probably much the same in all living things."
> Francis Crick (1916–2004)

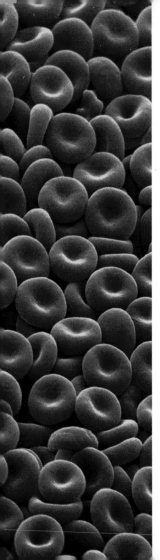

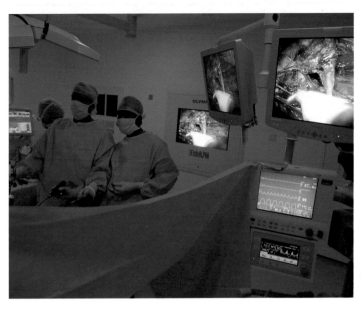

A surgeon performing a laparoscopy, or 'keyhole surgery', to remove a kidney for transplant. He is looking not at the patient but at a screen displaying images from the patient's interior; the blue light makes the images on the plasma screens easier to see. Photograph by David Bishop of UCL Medical School. Wellcome Image Award winner, 2011.

to offer an asbestos manufacturer a "quid pro quo" in order to pursue his investigations into links between the substance and lung cancer. Other glimpses are entirely personal, such as a letter to Arthur Mourant, who performed

Red blood cells: scanning electron micrograph by David McCarthy and Annie Cavanagh of the School of Pharmacy, University of London. Wellcome Image Award winner, 2008.

crucial work on blood groups, from the then-teenage cellist Jacqueline du Pré, a family friend.

Today, biomedical images are among science's most elegant products, expressing the harmony that collaborative research can achieve. They are celebrated in the Wellcome Image Awards, given to the best of the images submitted each year. ⓦ

Further reading and acknowledgements

Further reading

Anderson J, Barnes E, Shackleton E. The Art of Medicine: Over 2000 years of medicine in our lives. Lewes, East Sussex: Ilex; 2011.

Arnold K, Olsen D (eds). Medicine Man. London: British Museum Press; 2003.

Gould T (ed.). Cures and Curiosities: Inside the Wellcome Library. London: Profile; 2007.

Larson F. An Infinity of Things: How Sir Henry Wellcome collected the world. Oxford: Oxford University Press; 2009.

Picture credits

Cover Thom Atkinson; p. 16 (L) Rama Knight, (R) Antony Gormley studio; p. 17 White Cube Gallery; p. 18 (L) Adrian Brooks; p. 19 Deutsches Hygiene-Museum, photo by David Brandt, Dresden; p. 26 (TR) & pp. 28–9 Rama Knight; p. 46 (BR) Thom Atkinson; p. 50 Pitt Rivers Museum, Oxford; p. 57 (R) Duggan-Cronin Collection, McGregor Museum, Kimberley, South Africa; p. 59 (BR) Thom Atkinson; pp. 64–5 Rama Knight; p. 67 Annie Cattrell, photo by Freiburg Kunstverein; pp. 68–9 Institute for Plastination, Heidelberg; p. 71 Luke Jerram; p. 110 David McCarthy and Annie Cavanagh; p. 111 David Bishop. All other pictures: Wellcome Library

Thanks

The authors and editors would like to thank all the staff and supporters who helped to make this book possible, especially:

Ken Arnold (Head of Public Programmes, Wellcome Trust), Josephine Finn (Marketing Communications Project Manager, Wellcome Trust), Rachel Collins (Communications Manager, Wellcome Collection), James Peto (Senior Curator, Wellcome Collection), Lisa Jamieson (Events Manager, Wellcome Collection), Simon Chaplin (Head of Wellcome Library), Ross MacFarlane (Research Engagement Officer, Wellcome Library), Vicki Porter (Head of Discovery and Engagement, Wellcome Library), Richard Aspin (Head of Research and Scholarship, Wellcome Library), Danny Rees (Assistant Engagement Officer, Wellcome Library) and William Schupbach (Iconographic Collections Librarian, Wellcome Library).

▶
This caricature of Henry Wellcome as a bird, by Fred Reynolds, appeared in the trade journal *Chemist and Druggist* in June 1900. The stars and stripes refer to the country of Wellcome's birth.